THE 7 LAWS OF THE LEARNER™
Dr. Bruce H. Wilkinson
Course Notebook

■ **The Applied Principles of Learning Curriculum (APL)**™
The Applied Principles of Learning Curriculum provides unique training for Christian Educators–pastors, Sunday school teachers, public or private school teachers, Bible study leaders, or parents. This curriculum was developed to help you improve your skills in order to communicate in the most effective and compelling manner possible. Two separate courses have been developed in the APL Curriculum by two of America's outstanding communicators.

■ **The 7 Laws of the Learner**™
This course, developed and taught in live seminars by Dr. Bruce Wilkinson, founder and president of Walk Thru the Bible Ministries, focuses on the needs, traits, and prerogatives of the student. Examined are the Laws of the Learner, Expectation, Application, Retention, Need, Equipping, and Revival. Materials developed include an in-depth Teacher's Notebook and Teaching Overheads, along with a Course Notebook, Textbook, Audio Tapes, and more.

■ **The 7 Laws of the Teacher**™
This course, developed and taught on videotape by Dr. Howard G. Hendricks, nationally known Christian Educator and professor at Dallas Seminary, centers on the role, purpose, and impact of the teacher. It deals with the Laws of the Teacher, Education, Activity, Communication, Heart, Encouragement, and Readiness. This series consists of seven video lessons, Leader's Guide for use by the course facilitator, Course Notebook, and Course Textbook.

■ **Walk Thru the Bible Ministries, Inc.**®
The Applied Principles of Learning Curriculum has been produced and developed by Walk Thru the Bible Ministries, which exists to contribute to the spiritual growth of Christians worldwide through Bible teaching, tools, and training. We stand ready to help churches, schools, groups, and individual Christians enrich their walk with God. For more information on the ministries of Walk Thru the Bible, see pages 86-89 in this APL Course Notebook.

Walk Thru the Bible Ministries, Inc.
61 Perimeter Park, N.E.
P.O. Box 80587
Atlanta, Georgia 30366
(404) 458-9300

The Applied Principles of Learning Series ™
The 7 Laws of the Learner ™
Dr. Bruce H. Wilkinson
Course Notebook

Executive Editor: Dr. Bruce H. Wilkinson
Project Director: Gordon Wilkinson
Editor: Peter Wallace
Designer: Randy Drake

Published by
Walk Thru the Bible Ministries, Inc.®
P.O. Box 80587, Atlanta, Georgia 30366

Unless otherwise noted, all Scriptures quoted are taken
from The New King James Version, © 1979, 1980, 1982
by Thomas Nelson, Inc. Used by permission.

A Word from
Dr. Bruce H. Wilkinson

There's nothing more fulfilling for teachers, parents, pastors, or any other communicators than seeing their students blossom and flourish because of what and how they have taught them.

Would you like to experience that feeling when you teach? You can! We're about to discover seven laws that will enable you to teach for lifechange. These proven principles will revolutionize the way your students respond to your teaching, no matter what your specific situation may be.

You see, I've been studying the process of education for years now, honing and refining my own approach, and trying to put into practice what I've discovered. Every time I teach or communicate with others, my goal is to impress the truth of the Bible on them so that their lives change to reflect that truth. And over the years, I've discovered these Biblical methods to enable that to happen.

You've worked hard to be a good teacher. Now you are about to take the next steps toward becoming a master teacher, following the example of Jesus Christ Himself. So prepare to be challenged, to laugh, to question, to ponder, to be stretched, to become even more enthusiastic about your role as a communicator as we walk through The 7 Laws of the Learner. You—and your students—will never be the same again!

Dr. Bruce H. Wilkinson
Founder and President
Walk Thru the Bible Ministries

DR. BRUCE H. WILKINSON *is the founder and president of Walk Thru the Bible Ministries, headquartered in Atlanta, Georgia. He is executive editor of The Daily Walk Bible, of the book introductions of The Open Bible–Expanded Edition, and of Walk Thru's nationally renowned monthly devotional guides, including The Daily Walk, Closer Walk, Family Walk, and Youthwalk. A former faculty member of a Christian college, Bruce is now in great demand as a speaker across the country. He and his wife Darlene are the parents of David, Jennifer, and Jessica.*

How to Use Your Course Notebook

Use this notebook to help you review The 7 Laws of the Learner often, and grow to become a master communicator.

This notebook is designed to help you get the most out of The 7 Laws of the Learner course. Each of the seven sessions has a 12-page section of notes which includes:

Mindset: An introduction to the law featuring a Biblical passage illustrating the law in action.

Model: A chart demonstrating clearly what the law means and how it works.

Maxims: Seven principles that succinctly explain each law, along with a summary definition.

Meaning: A brief, memorable definition of the law.

Method: Specific steps you can take to put this law into practice in your own teaching situations.

Maximizers: A special section of tips to enable you to use each law most effectively.

Mastery: Special thought-provokers to help you interact with the meaning of each law. Record your thoughts in a notebook, or use these questions as discussion-starters with others who attend The 7 Laws course with you.

Memory: This "walk through" of each of The 7 Laws of the Learner will help you grasp the essence of each law, so that every time you teach you'll be able to think through the laws and thus better prepare to teach for lifechange.

Use this notebook to help you review The 7 Laws of the Learner often, and grow to become a master communicator.

The 7 Laws of the Learner

Course Notebook Contents

Get Your Personalized Certificate of Achievement . . . Free!

We'll send you a beautiful, personalized APL Certificate of Achievement free of charge for attending The 7 Laws of the Learner Seminar!

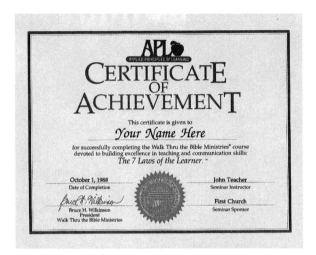

By getting involved in this seminar on The 7 Laws of the Learner, you've taken a major step on your way to becoming a master communicator.

To recognize your commitment, we've produced a beautiful APL Certificate of Achievement that you'll want to frame and display. This high quality certificate will be personlized with your name. And it's free for those who complete the course!

In the back of this Course Notebook you'll find an APL Certificate Order Form. After you've completed your training in The 7 Laws of the Learner, fill in this form and return it to your leader, or send it directly to Walk Thru the Bible Ministries. (See page 91 for more information.)

We're delighted that you have joined with others in pursuing excellence in teaching. Your adventure in teaching is just beginning!

Mindset

"Now, O Israel, listen to the statutes and the judgments which I teach you to observe, that you may live, and go in and possess the land which the LORD God of your fathers is giving you."

Deuteronomy 4:1

"And Moses called all Israel, and said to them: 'Hear, O Israel, the statutes and judgments which I speak in your hearing today, that you may learn them and be careful to observe them.' "

Deuteronomy 5:1

Model

LEARNER

Maxims

LEARNER

Learner Maxim 1:

Teachers are responsible to cause the students

to _____

> "The teacher who makes little or no allowance for individual differences in the classroom is an individual who makes little or no difference in the lives of his students."
> – William A. Ward

Learner Maxim 2:

Teachers will stand accountable to God for

their _____

Learner Maxim 3:

Teachers are responsible because they
control subject, style, setting, and

_____

> "Personally I'm always ready to learn, although I do not always like to be taught."
> – Winston Churchill

Learner Maxim 4:

Teachers should judge their success by the
success of their _____

Learner Maxim 5:

Teachers impact more by their character
and commitment than their

_____

Learner Maxim 6:

Teachers exist to serve the

_____

Learner Maxim 7:

Teachers who practice the APL Laws can
become master _____

Learner Meaning

" _____ _____ _____ "

The teacher should accept the responsibility
of causing students to learn.

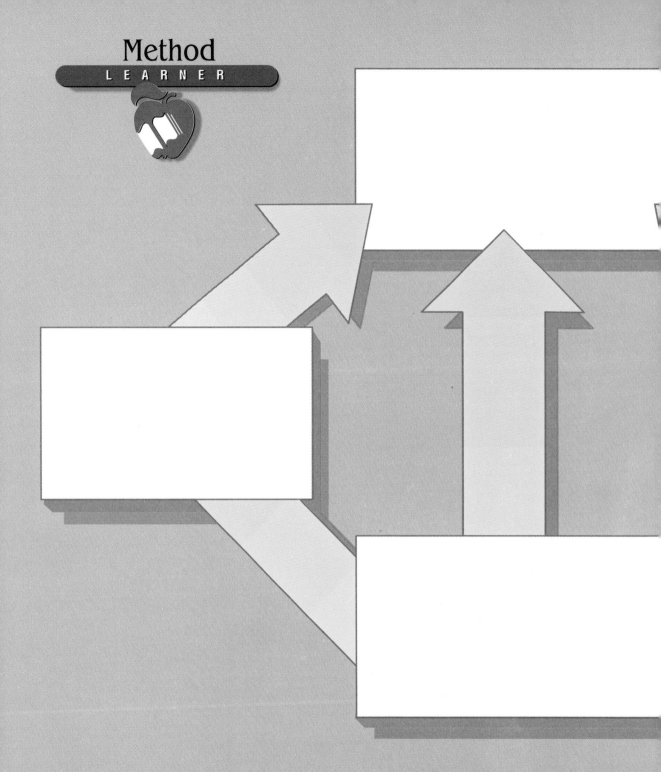

Maximizers

ove your students consistently and

_____

xpress the subject in terms of the
students' needs and _____

*"Anyone who stops
learning is old, whether
at twenty or eighty."
– Henry Ford*

lter your style regularly according to
each _____

est in your talents and gifts and be

_____

ote constantly your students' attitudes, attention, and _____

 xcel by using your strengths to compensate for your _____

ely on the Holy Spirit for teaching that is _____

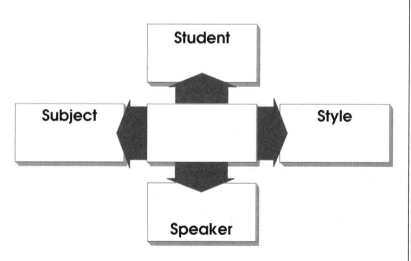

Student

Subject

Style

Speaker

Mastery

MINDSET:

Remember the definitions of teaching we discussed? "To provide information . . . to cover material . . . to impart truth." Those are commonly practiced definitions of teaching, and yet we discovered that God has a far more challenging definition in mind: to cause the student to learn. Think of your own teaching career and evaluate it in light of this definition. Have you really been teaching? What needs to change in your own thinking in order for you to fulfill the proper definition of teaching?

MAXIMS:

Think back over your educational career and choose the best teacher you ever had. What top three characteristics made that person a master teacher? How important was his/her commitment to "cause you to learn"? What would happen to those three outstanding characteristics had he/she lost that commitment?

God holds people accountable only for that which is in their control. When you observe some classes, you sometimes get the impression that the teacher has little or no control, and therefore their accountability will be minimal! On the other hand, some teachers exercise remarkable control over their classes. How would the mindsets of both kinds of teachers be different regarding the degree of control one can and should have over oneself, one's subject, one's style, and the class setting? If we watched your last class, what would we assume your mindset to be on those issues?

METHOD:

Consider the three major emphases that teachers exhibit: subject-oriented, student-oriented, and style-oriented. Think of a teacher in your experience who is an example of each type, and describe some of the things they did to identify them as such. Which type are you? Do you sense an imbalance in your teaching method?

5 Think again about your method orientation—subject, student, or style. List five strengths of that particular orientation. Now list five potential problems of it. Do you ever find yourself wrestling with any of those problems yourself? Think of some steps you could take to turn each of those weaknesses into another strength.

MAXIMIZERS:

6 As we discovered, style is a crucial element to effective teaching. How rigid are you in your teaching style? What about your style would you consider to be positive strengths? What areas of your style would you like to improve? What do you think it would take for you to improve your teaching style? Also, how adaptable are you to changing your style according to each teaching situation?

7 Who are your "heroes" of teaching—those skilled communicators who serve as models for you? Now ask yourself, are you subconsciously—or even consciously—attempting to duplicate the methods and style of that teacher? What do you think might happen if you stopped trying to emulate someone else and started letting God work through you just as He created you? There's nothing wrong with honing your skills by observing other skilled teachers, but avoid trying to copy another teacher because the result is usually as flat as a photo of that teacher. What will you do in order to make yourself available to the Lord and allow the Holy Spirit to teach supernaturally through you?

To get the most out of these questions, take the time to think through them, then capture your thoughts in a journal or notebook. Or get together with several other people attending this APL course and discuss your answers.

Memory

The Law of the Learner

" _____ _____ _____ "

Step 1: _____

Step 2: _____

Step 3: _____

Step 4: _____

Step 5: _____

I commit to _____

_____

_____

Expectation

LAW TWO

Mindset

EXPECTATION

²⁴ And let us consider one another in order to stir up love and good works, ²⁵ not forsaking the assembling of ourselves together, as is the manner of some, but exhorting one another, and so much the more as you see the Day approaching.

Hebrews 10:24–25

¹² Beware, brethren, lest there be in any of you an evil heart of unbelief in departing from the living God; ¹³ but exhort one another daily, while it is called "Today," lest any of you be hardened through the deceitfulness of sin.

Hebrews 3:12–13

Model

EXPECTATION

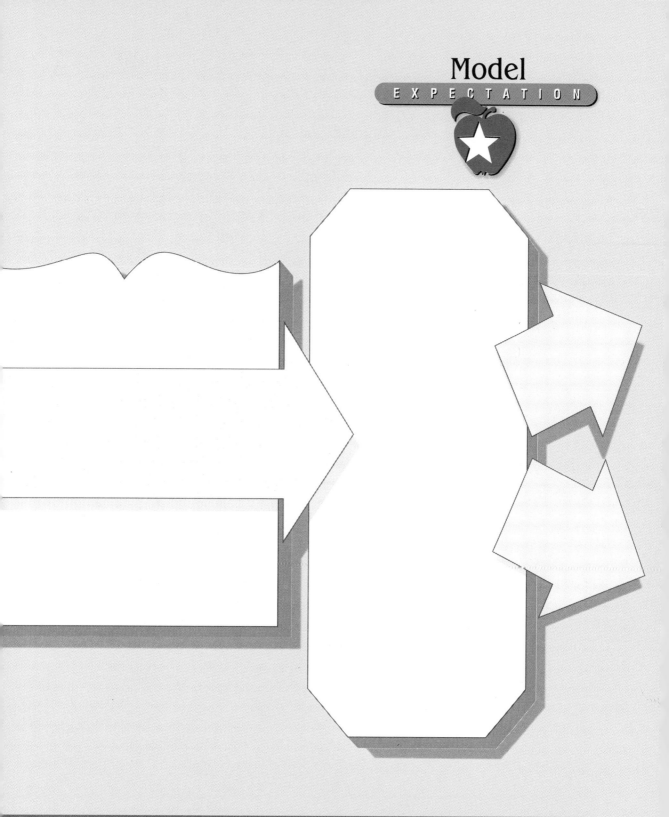

Maxims

*"Both he who expects
great things of others,
and he who expects
little, will receive what
he expects."*
– Anonymous

Expectation Maxim 1:

Expectations exist in everyone about
everything all the _____

Expectation Maxim 2:

Expectations impact ourselves and

_____

Expectation Maxim 3:

Expectations are rooted in the past,
influence the present, and therefore
impact the _____

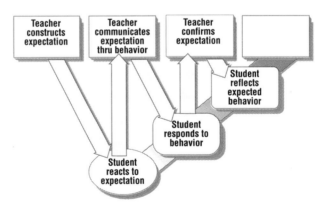

Expectation Maxim 4:

Expectations are exposed through our
attitudes and _____

Expectation Maxim 5:

Expectations influence the future whether stated or _____

Expectation Maxim 6:

Expectations impair others if set too low or too high for too _____

Expectation Maxim 7:

Expectations empower others if guided by

_____

Expectation Meaning

" _____ _____ _____ "

The teacher should influence students' learning by adjusting expectations.

The 5 Most Important Words in the English Language: "I am proud of you."

The 4 Most Important Words in the English Language: "What do you think?"

The 3 Most Important Words in the English Language: "If you please."

The 2 Most Important Words in the English Language: "Thank you."

The Most Important Word in the English Language: "You."

– Adapted from Reader's Digest

Method

EXPECTATION

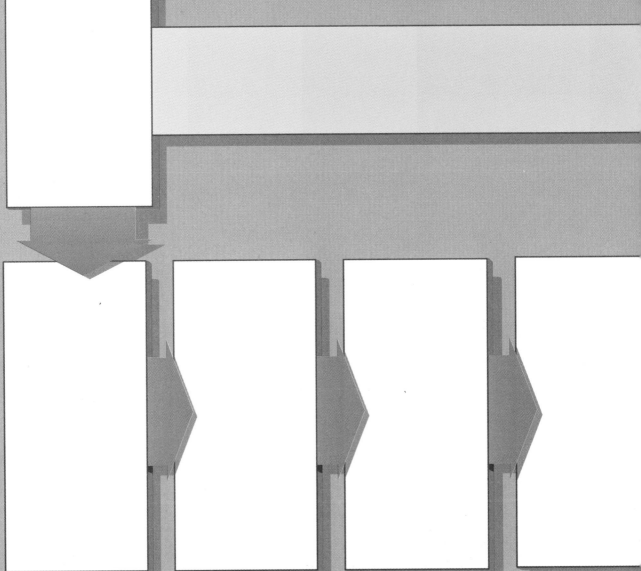

Maximizers

 mploy opportunities

_____.

"If silent expectations
have a direct impact on
others—and they do—
just consider how
multiplied an impact
a positive expectation
that one vocalizes
can have."
– Dr. Bruce Wilkinson

 press expectations

_____.

 ick words

_____.

 stablish eye contact

_____.

---

ommunicate body language

_____ .

 ouch others

_____ .

 et expectations

_____ .

Mastery
EXPECTATION

MODEL:

1 Now that you've been exposed to the APL Law of Expectation, jot down any expectations you have had about your own class or teaching situation.

In view of the Expectation Model, how could you reformulate your expectations so that you can consider your students and exhort them daily in order to excite them to do good works and avoid evil?

MAXIMS:

2 Assume some different roles and notice how expectations can influence us:

(1) You read one of those "Get Rich Quick" ads in the newspaper which says the best speaker on investments will present a day-long seminar for "only $195." You hit your piggy bank and attend. The speaker arrives— she's 19, wearing sweat pants and jogging shoes!

(2) You bump into your old high school coach who introduces you to his daughter (whom you've had a crush on for three years) as the "lamebrain who couldn't play football, soccer, basketball, or tennis, and who couldn't even walk without tripping."

(3) You are a rural, conservative farm girl visiting an old college friend now living in the heart of New York City. You get lost and accidentally find yourself in a punk rock club—and everybody notices you when you walk in.

How do you think we build those expectations?

3 Let's say the dreaded day has finally arrived: Tony the Terror has been promoted to your class. You've never seen him, but he's been the talk of the teachers' lounge for the past two years. When class starts, you can't wait to show him who's boss. In what ways is the deck stacked against him? What strategy would you use to change your own expectations of him and impact his expectations of you in a positive manner?

METHOD:

4 In your own experience, have you ever witnessed a time when your expectations of a student helped to blossom him or her? Have you ever had an opportunity in which you were—perhaps unknowingly—utilizing this law to encourage someone? If so, what was the short-term reaction? Were there long-term benefits that came about as a result of your positive expectations? Has anyone blossomed you? Describe your feelings about it.

5 Follow the five steps in the Expectation Method to construct verbal expressions of your expectations in the following situations: (1) Your child comes home with a black eye, having picked a fight in the schoolyard on the way home; (2) Your spouse failed to do his/her share of the household chores as agreed, instead choosing to watch an old movie on TV; (3) Your class has a bad case of spring fever just before a major test and didn't study; (4) Your Sunday school students routinely come into class 10 minutes late; (5) A struggling student spends all weekend on an extra credit project for class.

MAXIMIZERS:

6 One of the Maximizers encourages us to express our expectations creatively. In the session we discovered a number of ways to do that, including thinking it, praying it, writing it, saying it directly, and saying it indirectly. Think of three of your students who need a bit of encouragement, select three of those methods (or devise your own), and put them into practice this week. Keep a record of how and when you expressed your expectations to them, and try to track the results. By the way, this is a great habit to get into!

7 Consider the seven Expectation Maximizers. Which one presents the greatest challenge to you? Perhaps it's choosing your words carefully, or establishing eye contact, or touching others appropriately. Whatever it may be, plan specific ways to use that particular Maximizer the next time you teach. Write out the steps you'll take to do it, and don't be afraid to practice it first! Before long you'll find it's a natural part of your teaching.

To get the most out of these questions, take the time to think through them, then capture your thoughts in a journal or notebook. Or get together with several other people attending this APL course and discuss your answers.

Memory
EXPECTATION

The Law of Expectation

" _____ _____ _____ "

Step 1: _____

Step 2: _____

Step 3: _____

Step 4: _____

Step 5: _____

I commit to _____

_____

_____

Application

LAW THREE

Mindset
APPLICATION

¹⁶All Scripture is given by inspiration of God, and is profitable for doctrine, for reproof, for correction, for instruction in righteousness, ¹⁷that the man of God may be complete, thoroughly equipped for every good work.

2 Timothy 3:16–17

Model
APPLICATION

Maxims

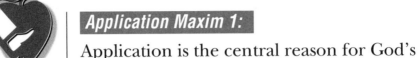

Application Maxim 1:

Application is the central reason for God's

_____

"The Scriptures were not given for our information, but for our transformation."
– D. L. Moody

Application Maxim 2:

Application is the responsibility of the

_____

Application Maxim 3:

Application and information should be appropriately _____

"Every great person has first learned how to obey, whom to obey, and when to obey."
– William A. Ward

Application Maxim 4:

Application focuses Scripture on the students'

_____

Application Maxim 5:

Application has maximum influence when
the student personally sees its Biblical

_____

Application Maxim 6:

Application that has impacted the teacher
tends to impact the student more

_____

Application Maxim 7:

Application must ultimately lead the student
from studying the Bible to obeying the

_____

Application Meaning

" _____ _____ _____ "

The teacher should stimulate lifechange in
students by properly applying the Scriptures.

*"Any time truths become the
end of our teaching, rather
than the means to an end, we
have short-circuited the
God-ordained purpose of
those truths."
– Dr. Bruce Wilkinson*

Method
APPLICATION

Maximizers

 A sk God to develop in you an applier's

_____

 P repare applications in relation to your
students' _____

> *"Understanding can
> wait. Obedience
> cannot."*
> *– Geoffrey Grogan*

 P lan all parts of the lesson to contribute
to the _____

 L ead your students beyond general
application to specific steps of

_____

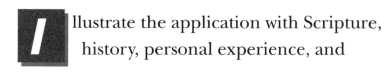 llustrate the application with Scripture, history, personal experience, and

_____

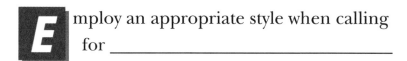 mploy an appropriate style when calling for _____

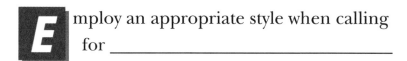 trengthen applications with student

_____

Mastery

MINDSET:

1 As we discovered in 2 Timothy 3:16,17, the Bible was given for lifechange, and God has given us four different tracks to bring about two different changes. Doctrine and correction relate to belief, positively and negatively. Instruction in righteousness and reproof relate to behavior, positively and negatively. With that in mind, how would you use each of these four approaches to teach an adult class on these subjects: Parenting, Giving, and Renewing the Mind?

MAXIMS:

2 Two evangelical Bible-believing Sunday school teachers present the same lesson on the same Sunday to the same age group. One believes it is his personal responsibility to explain the Bible and the Holy Spirit's responsibility to apply it. The other believes it is his responsibility to rely on the Holy Spirit for the entire lesson, but feels responsible both to explain and apply it himself in class. You conduct some market research and interview four people from each class. What differences would you probably find in their thinking and living?

3 In an age when everyone is pushing for only one absolute in life—namely, that there aren't any absolutes—the Bible still contains numerous absolutes. The Book hasn't changed, but our society has . . . and we are reaping the fruit of our error. One reason so many Christians live defeated lives these days is that Bible teachers are waxing eloquent on their own ideas rather than the Lord's. Why is a teacher's normal tendency to push his or her own ideas rather than God's truths? Why do you think more lives would move in the direction of godliness if people wrestled with the very Word of God? By the way . . . was your class faced with "thus saith the Lord" from the Bible during your last lesson?

METHOD:

4 One of the key steps in the APL Application Method is Step 3—personalizing the principle that you've drawn from the passage. As your students see how relevant the truth is, the Holy Spirit can

SPECIAL NOTE:

Each of these thought-provoking questions is related to one of the major segments of the Law of Application. They are structured to help you internalize the true APL mindset.

begin His ministry of conviction. Consider your own teaching situation—or one you'd like to be in eventually. How would you personalize these principles to your group so that they see the relevance of the truth to their own lives: (1) God is unchanging and unchangeable, (2) Jesus Christ is our Great High Priest, (3) Life is like a vapor, (4) The fear of God is the beginning of wisdom?

5 Think of the last lesson you taught. Write down the main Scripture reference(s) you used. Now compare your lesson with the five steps of the APL Application Method. How many did you follow? Restructure your lesson by using these five steps: Passage, Principle, Personalize, Persuade, Perform. Now compare your new plan with the one you used. Do you think there would have been a difference in the impact on your students if you had used your new lesson plan? What would that difference be, and why?

MAXIMIZERS:

6 One of the APL Application Maximizers encourages you to prioritize your applications according to your students' needs. We'll think more thoroughly about this aspect of teaching in the APL Law of Need. But for now, think about your current teaching situation and consider your class members. What do you think would be the top three needs in the lives of those students? What would your students' reaction be to your teaching if you focused directly on those needs for the next six weeks, rather than teaching what you had planned?

7 As we discovered, Jesus Christ was a master at using illustrations to teach. And most of His illustrations were fictional stories developed specifically to make a point. Think about your next teaching opportunity. What will be the key point of your lesson? Try your hand at illustrating it by developing a fictional illustration, like a parable or allegory, to communicate the point dramatically.

To get the most out of these questions, take the time to think through them, then capture your thoughts in a journal or notebook. Or get together with several other people attending this APL course and discuss your answers.

Memory

APPLICATION

The Law of Application

" _____ _____ _____ "

Step 1: _____

Step 2: _____

Step 3: _____

Step 4: _____

Step 5: _____

I commit to _____

_____

_____

Retention

LAW FOUR

Mindset

RETENTION

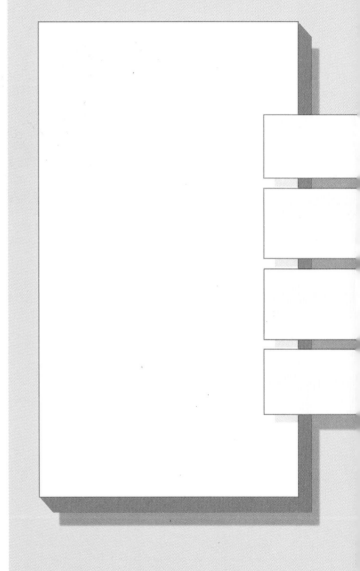

"⁴Hear, O Israel: The LORD our God, the LORD is one! ⁵You shall love the LORD your God with all your heart, with all your soul, and with all your might. ⁶And these words which I command you today shall be in your heart; ⁷you shall teach them diligently to your children, and shall talk of them when you sit in your house, when you walk by the way, when you lie down, and when you rise up. ⁸You shall bind them as a sign on your hand, and they shall be as frontlets between your eyes. ⁹You shall write them on the doorposts of your house and on your gates."

Deuteronomy 6:4-9

Model

RETENTION

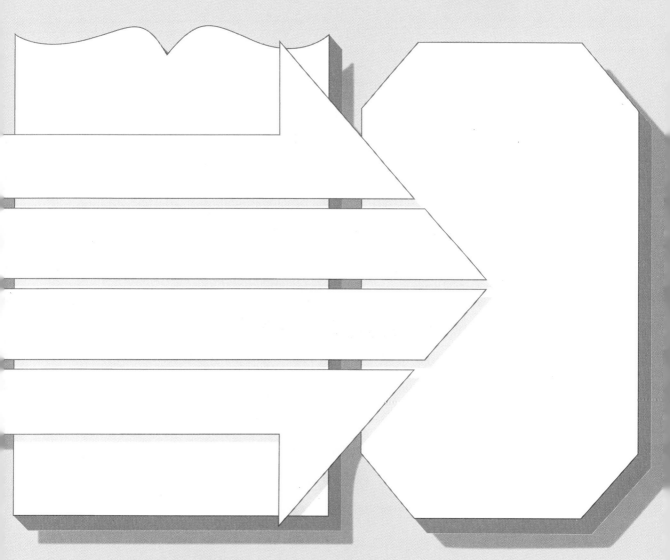

Maxims

RETENTION

Retention Maxim 1:

Retention of facts by the student is the teacher's _____

Retention Maxim 2:

Retention of facts is effective only after they are _____

Retention Maxim 3:

Retention increases as the student recognizes the content's _____

Retention Maxim 4:

Retention requires the teacher to focus on the facts that are most _____

Retention Maxim 5:

Retention arranges the facts so they are easy

to _____

Retention Maxim 6:

Retention strengthens long-term memory

through regular _____

"We teachers must present the whole before its parts and help our students master the irreducible minimum."
– Dr. Bruce Wilkinson

Retention Maxim 7:

Retention minimizes time for memorization

to maximize time for _____

Gather	Outline	Cover	Prior-itize	Mnemon-icize	Mem-orize	Practice Use	Indepen-dent Use

Retention Meaning

" _____ _____ _____ "

The teacher should enable students to enjoy maximum mastery of the irreducible minimum.

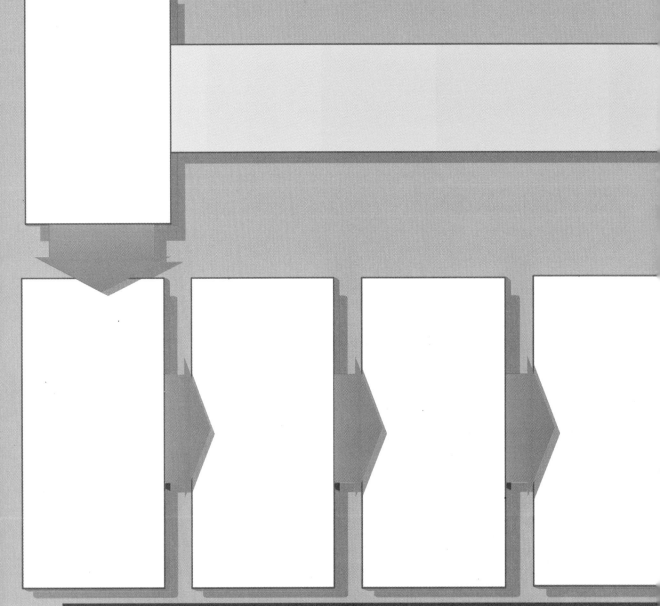

Maximizers

 Represent the facts in a

_____

"I have a photographic memory, but sometimes I forget to take off the lens cap."

 Express the facts with

_____

 Transfer facts by the

_____

 Associate facts with objects and

_____

mpress the facts through

_____

 ote the facts through

_____

 ummarize the facts with graphs and

_____

"Every Bible book, doctrine, or event has a main structure which should not only be shown, but taught until the student masters it."
– Dr. Bruce Wilkinson

Mastery

Each of these thought-provoking questions is related to one of the major segments of the Law of Retention. They are structured to help you internalize the true APL mindset.

MINDSET:

Most teachers in educational institutions at all levels assume their job is simply to "cover" the material. How does this current mindset of teaching hinder the students' retention of facts? How should the APL Mindset of "causing the students to learn" impact the students' retention of facts? Consider your own teaching style for a moment. On a scale of 1 to 10, with 1 representing the false mindset and 10 representing the APL mindset, where would you fall? What specific steps will you take to see the APL Mindset represented in Deuteronomy 6:4-9—with the dual goals of loving God and knowing His Word—operative in your own teaching ministry?

MAXIMS:

When people have a flat tire, they look for a pump. If they don't have a flat tire, there's no reason to look for a pump. What happens to the rate of learning that occurs when the student sees absolutely no relevance or value for the facts you are asking him to memorize? If he sees no relevance, whose fault is it? If they don't have a flat tire, then don't give them the pump. Let the air out of their tires first. Then offer the pump! What steps can you take to increase your students' realization of the relevance of the subject to their own lives?

Real life is full of real problems to solve. And as far as most of us adults are concerned, we don't really have a need to memorize information. Instead, we just want to know where to go to find the information we need. Since that is true, the ability that needs to be strengthened in our students is not memorizing but applying facts. How would your students react to less time cramming and more time using the information presented in class? How would you rate a teacher who taught this way? How would you rate yourself?

METHOD:

Becoming proficient at establishing the Irreducible Minimum of a subject for your group is a key part of mastering the Law of Retention. Let's assume you are the Director of Christian Education of a church and your goal is to see that every age group from children to senior adult will study one particular subject or book of the Bible for one quarter. Think through what the Irreducible Minimum might be for these age groups—Kindergarten, Third Grade, Sixth Grade, High School, Young Married, Middle-Age Adult, and Senior Citizen—for one of these course subjects: The Book of John, Creation, the Attributes of God, God's Plan for the Family.

5 Another crucial factor for succeeding with the Law of Retention is to arrange facts so they're easy to memorize—that is, to make them "Mindeasy." As we've seen, there are a number of ways to accomplish this. Select one of the subjects and one of the age groups listed in the question above and let your imagination run free as you try to make the appropriate Irreducible Minimum "mindeasy" for that audience. Select another subject and age group and try it again.

MAXIMIZERS:

6 Think carefully about the 10 Principles for Maximum Memorization—Involvement, Association, Spontaneity, Intensity, Exaggeration, Emotion, Humor, Rhyme, Rhythm, and Variety. In your own words, explain how each one contributes to the students' retention of the facts you are teaching. Pick four of them and give concrete examples of how they would work.

7 Which of the significant seven Maximizers would you personally find easier to utilize in your teaching? Which would be harder? Select three of the methods you find to be harder and determine how you would specifically implement them in your next teaching situation, considering your audience and subject matter. Once you get used to the process, you'll find it becomes easier to use all seven Retention Maximizers!

To get the most out of these questions, take the time to think through them, then capture your thoughts in a journal or notebook. Or get together with several other people attending this APL course and discuss your answers.

Memory
RETENTION

The Law of Retention

"_____ _____ _____"

Step 1: _____

Step 2: _____

Step 3: _____

Step 4: _____

Step 5: _____

I commit to _____

_____

_____

Mindset

NEED

⁵ So He came to a city of Samaria which is called Sychar, near the plot of ground that Jacob gave to his son Joseph. ⁶ Now Jacob's well was there. Jesus therefore, being wearied from His journey, sat thus by the well. It was about the sixth hour. ⁷A woman of Samaria came to draw water. Jesus said to her, "Give Me a drink." ⁸ For His disciples had gone away into the city to buy food.

⁹ Then the woman of Samaria said to Him, "How is it that You, being a Jew, ask a drink from me, a Samaritan woman?" For Jews have no dealings with Samaritans. ¹⁰Jesus answered and said to her, "If you knew the gift of God, and who it is who says to you, 'Give Me a drink,' you would have asked Him, and He would have given you living water."

¹¹ The woman said to Him, "Sir, You have nothing to draw with, and the well is deep. Where then do You get that living water? ¹²Are You greater than our father Jacob, who gave us the well, and drank from it himself, as well as his sons and his livestock?"

¹³ Jesus answered and said to her, "Whoever drinks of this water will thirst again, ¹⁴ but whoever drinks of the water that I shall give him will never thirst. But the water that I shall give him will become in him a fountain of water springing up into everlasting life."

¹⁵ The woman said to Him, "Sir, give me this water, that I may not thirst, nor come here to draw."

¹⁶ Jesus said to her, "Go, call your husband, and come here." ¹⁷ The woman answered and said, "I have no husband." Jesus said to her, "You have well said, 'I have no husband,' ¹⁸ for you have had five husbands, and the one whom you now have is not your husband; in that you spoke truly."

¹⁹ The woman said to Him, "Sir, I perceive that You are a prophet. ²⁰ Our fathers worshiped on this mountain, and you Jews say that in Jerusalem is the place where one ought to worship."

²¹ Jesus said to her, "Woman, believe Me, the hour is coming when you will neither on this mountain, nor in Jerusalem, worship the Father. ²²You worship what you do not know; we know what we worship, for salvation is of the Jews. ²³But the hour is coming, and now is, when the true worshipers will worship the Father in spirit and truth; for the Father is seeking such to worship Him. ²⁴God is Spirit, and those who worship Him must worship in spirit and truth."

²⁵The woman said to Him, "I know that Messiah is coming" (who is called Christ). "When He comes, He will tell us all things."

²⁶Jesus said to her, "I who speak to you am He."

John 4:5-26

Model

NEED

Maxims

N E E D

"A great teacher is not simply one who imparts knowledge to his students, but one who awakens their interest in it and makes them eager to pursue it for themselves. He is a spark plug, not a fuel pipe."
– M. J. Berrill

Need Maxim 1:

Need building is the responsibility of the

_____

Need Maxim 2:

Need meeting is the teacher's primary

_____

Need Maxim 3:

Need building is the teacher's main method to

motivate _____

"The basic problem most people have is that they're doing nothing to solve their basic problem."
– Bob Richardson

Need Maxim 4:

Need motivates to the degree it is felt by the

_____

Need Maxim 5:

Need building always precedes new units of

_____

Need Maxim 6:

Need should be built according to the
audience's characteristics and

_____

Need Maxim 7:

Need building may be hindered by factors
beyond the teacher's _____

Need Meaning

" _____ _____ _____ "

The teacher should surface the students' real
need before teaching the content.

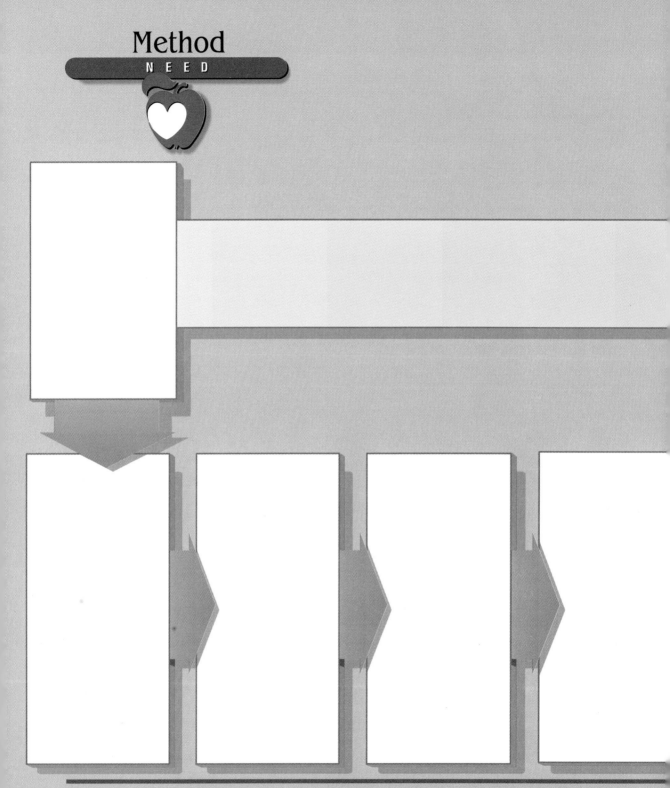

Method

NEED

Maximizers

N E E D

D escribe the need in a factual

_____

E xpress the need through

_____

"The lesson does not have a need—the students do. The lesson is only the tool you use to meet the needs of your students."
– Dr. Bruce Wilkinson

S ensitize to the need through

_____

I ncrease the need through your

_____

R aise the need through

_____

 E xhibit the need with a

_____

 S ymbolize the need with a

_____

Mastery

NEED

MODEL:

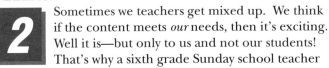

1 The process Jesus Christ followed in building need with the Samaritan woman (John 4) was reduced to five steps in the APL Need Model. Consider how Christ followed those steps, then scope out how you might utilize them in dealing with your class on the subject of having a daily devotional time with the Lord. How would you "seize attention"? How would you "stir curiosity"? What "felt need" would you stimulate? How would you "surface the real need" and then "satisfy the real need" of having a daily time in God's Word and prayer?

MAXIMS:

2 Sometimes we teachers get mixed up. We think if the content meets *our* needs, then it's exciting. Well it is—but only to us and not our students! That's why a sixth grade Sunday school teacher may find himself excitedly talking over his students' heads. Have you ever found yourself turned on to a subject that is totally tuned out by your class? What telltale signs from your students indicate that you are building a need that really isn't lighting their fire? And when you notice those telltale signs, what should your response be?

3 Imagine that you're waxing eloquent and your class is totally out of it. You get hotter and they just wilt faster. You can't understand it. After all, it's only 96 degrees on a Friday afternoon at 2:30, the last day of school, with a big celebration party next on their agenda. So why can't they get excited about your lesson? Remember, when it's not working, *you* may not be the "broken" part. What are the most common external causes that can destroy otherwise good teaching? What could you do about each of them—if anything? What would you do if you couldn't do anything about some of these external hindrances? How are these external hindrances different from the many internal causes that can hinder learning?

METHOD:

4 What are the five top needs of your students? Finding the needs of your students is a major key to utilizing this APL Law successfully. Review in your own thinking the direct and indirect methods of finding the needs. Which methods would be most effective with your own students? Begin now to build a need inventory for your class by developing an anonymous questionnaire, making some phone calls, and doing some general research.

5 Let's assume you've developed a need inventory, and you know the top needs of your class. Which one will you focus on (step 2) in your next class? How will you forecast the need (step 3)—in other words, how will you help your students anticipate the benefits of meeting this need? How will you help them feel the need (step 4)? And what will you do to fulfill the need in their lives (step 5)? Think carefully through those steps and put them to work in your next class. You'll be amazed at the response!

MAXIMIZERS:

6 The seven APL Need Maximizers are among the most important tools you can have in your tool chest to help in teaching. Consider these subjects; see if you can think of an example using each Maximizer to build the need for a lesson on: (1) adultery in Christian marriages; (2) ministry to AIDS patients; (3) stewardship and financial management; (4) parenting adolescents.

7 Think again through the seven Maximizers. As you worked through the exercise above, which ones came easier to you? Which ones do you think you'd have a bigger struggle using in your teaching? Select the one you think is the hardest to utilize, and decide on a way to use it in your next teaching opportunity to build the need you are aiming to fulfill. Then do it!

To get the most out of these questions, take the time to think through them, then capture your thoughts in a journal or notebook. Or get together with several other people attending this APL course and discuss your answers.

Memory
N E E D

The Law of Need

" _____ _____ _____ "

Step 1: _____

Step 2: _____

Step 3: _____

Step 4: _____

Step 5: _____

I commit to _____

_____

_____

Equipping

LAW SIX

Mindset

EQUIPPING

"[11] And He Himself (Jesus Christ) gave some to be apostles, some prophets, some evangelists, and some pastors and teachers, [12] for the equipping of the saints for the work of ministry, for the edifying of the body of Christ, [13] till we all come to the unity of the faith and the knowledge of the Son of God, to a perfect man, to the measure of the stature of the fullness of Christ; [14] that we should no longer be children, tossed to and fro and carried about with every wind of doctrine, by the trickery of men, in the cunning craftiness by which they lie in wait to deceive, [15] but, speaking the truth in love, may grow up in all things unto Him who is the head—Christ."

Ephesians 4:11-15

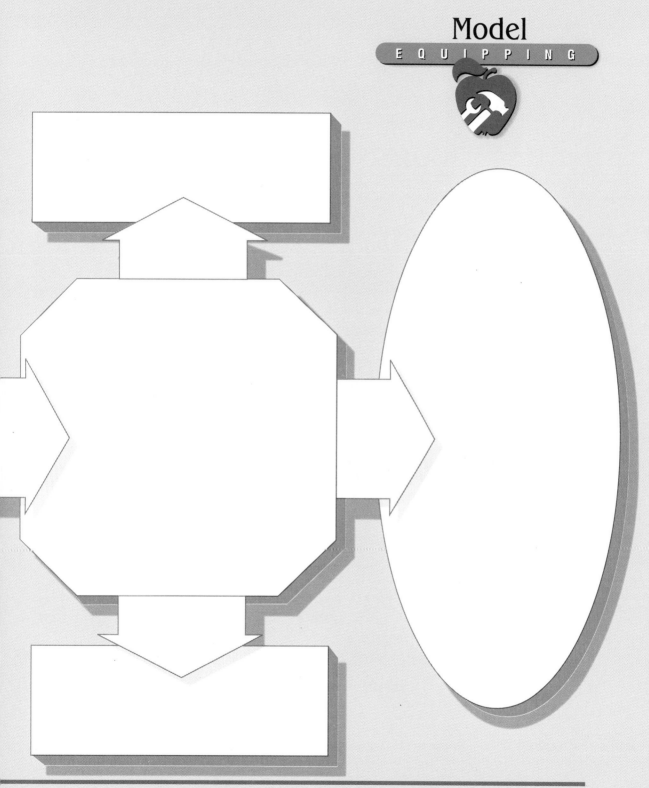

Model

EQUIPPING

Maxims

E Q U I P P I N G

Equipping Maxim 1:

Equipping is the responsibility of the

_____

Equipping Maxim 2:

Equipping occurs best when the teacher assumes the Biblical _____

Equipping Maxim 3:

Equipping is best evaluated by what the student does after _____

Equipping Maxim 4:

Equipping should impact both character and

_____

Equipping Maxim 5:

Equipping should focus more intensely on the most _____

"Ministry that costs nothing accomplishes nothing."
– John Henry Jowett

Equipping Maxim 6:

Equipping requires knowledge, skill, and long-term _____

Equipping Maxim 7:

Equipping has as its ultimate goal independent

_____

"The teacher or preacher is not called to spend the majority of his time evangelizing the lost; he is to equip his class to do the evangelizing."
– Dr. Bruce Wilkinson

Equipping Meaning

" _____ _____ _____ "

The teacher should train students for a life of service and edification.

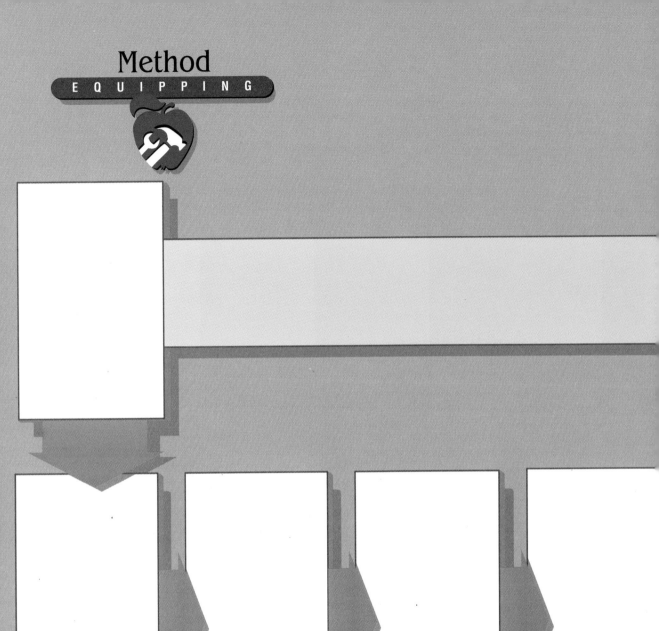

Method

EQUIPPING

Maximizers

EQUIPPING

T rain your students until they are successful independent users of the

_____

R eproduce yourself by focusing on their skill, not your _____

A lter equipping according to your students' characteristics and _____

I ncrease student motivation by relationship, retribution, and

_____

Nail down the basics before developing advanced _____

Encourage students more frequently during early _____

Reaffirm students independent of their level of _____

Mastery

E Q U I P P I N G

MINDSET:

1 Our study of Ephesians 4 revealed a number of key principles on equipping: (1) The primary purpose of the teacher is to equip; (2) The primary audience teachers equip is Christian; (3) The primary result of equipped Christians is that they are doing the work of ministry and edifying the body of Christ. Evaluate your own teaching ministry in light of these three principles. Ask yourself, "How true is this principle in my teaching? What needs to change in order for it to be true? How should I accomplish that change?"

MAXIMS:

2 Limited time and opportunity require that we carefully invest our lives. Paul said to pass the truth on to faithful ones. Therefore, spend your time equipping those who already prove to be the kind of people discussed in 1 Timothy and Titus. (It's important to have one or two special people, of course, who need some close attention in building them to that level.) Maximize your efforts by choosing your team carefully! List the top 3-5 people in your life whom you should be equipping for Him. Start with your family. Will you take the first steps today? Then schedule some time with each one to discuss your desire to equip them.

3 How do you know when one of your students is equipped, and you are ready to graduate him or her? Graduate them when they are playing big league ball between Monday and Friday and can, in turn, coach others. That's called multiplication. And it's living life God's way. Have you graduated any students lately? Are there any in the final semesters of "study"? If not, why not? And will you change your approach to your teaching responsibility so that your students become enrolled in the school of equipping?

METHOD:

4 Central to the whole concept of equipping is the ability to see exactly where your students are at any given time in their skill development and to know the appropriate solution for helping them improve. In other words, does the weakness in your students' play reflect a basic misunderstanding of the game, or a poor skill development, or an inappropriate attitude that is subtly coming out in his execution? How well are you able to determine how your students are coming along in the equipping process? What steps will you take to become more sensitive to their progress . . . or lack of it?

5 Think again through the five steps of the APL Equipping Method—Instruct, Illustrate, Involve, Improve, Inspire. Let's assume you will be teaching a series on how to communicate better. Make some specific plans as to how you will follow each step in order to equip your students to communicate. Now, why not try the process with the subject you'll be dealing with next in your teaching situation!

MAXIMIZERS:

6 Motivation to learn a skill is a key to success. Consider again the motivations of relationship, retribution, and reward. How would you define each of those motivations in your own words? Think about your own teaching situation and what you are trying to equip your students to do. In what specific ways could you use those three motivations to encourage them in their progress?

7 It there's one common error made in utilizing the Law of Equipping, it is that the teacher too frequently moves on to the next section when the students have merely been exposed to the skill rather than having experienced it. Even veteran professional football or baseball players review the basics every year in training camp. Quizzes or tests can help determine how far your students have come, but the best test is to see how well they actually utilize what they're learning in everyday life. Brainstorm some ways you can test your students' readiness to move on. Which of those ways will you use this week?

To get the most out of these questions, take the time to think through them, then capture your thoughts in a journal or notebook. Or get together with several other people attending this APL course and discuss your answers.

Memory

The Law of Equipping

" _____ _____ _____ "

Step 1: _____

Step 2: _____

Step 3: _____

Step 4: _____

Step 5: _____

I commit to _____

_____

_____

Revival

LAW SEVEN

Mindset

REVIVAL

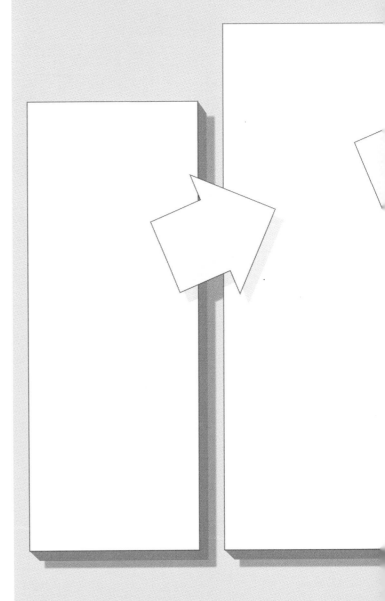

¹Then the LORD sent Nathan to David. And he came to him, and said to him: "There were two men in one city, one rich and the other poor. ²The rich man had exceedingly many flocks and herds. ³But the poor man had nothing, except one little ewe lamb which he had bought and nourished; and it grew up together with him and with his children. It ate of his own food and drank from his own cup and lay in his bosom; and it was like a daughter to him. ⁴And a traveler came to the rich man, who refused to take from his own flock and from his own herd to prepare one for the wayfaring man who had come to him; but he took the poor man's lamb and prepared it for the man who had come to him."

⁵Then David's anger was greatly aroused against the man, and he said to Nathan, "As the LORD lives, the man who has done this shall surely die! ⁶And he shall restore fourfold for the lamb, because he did this thing and because he had no pity."

⁷Then Nathan said to David, "You are the man! Thus says the LORD God of Israel: I anointed you king over Israel, and I delivered you from the hand of Saul. ⁸I gave you your master's house and your master's wives into your keeping, and gave you the house of Israel and Judah. And if that had been too little, I also would have given you much more!

⁹Why have you despised the commandment of the LORD, to do evil in His sight? You have killed Uriah the Hittite with the sword; you have taken his wife to be your wife, and have killed him with the sword of the people of Ammon.

¹⁰Now therefore, the sword shall never depart from your house, because you have despised Me, and have taken the wife of Uriah the Hittite to be your wife.' ¹¹"Thus says the LORD: 'Behold, I will raise up adversity against you from your own house; and I will take your wives before your eyes and give them to your neighbor, and he shall lie with your wives in the sight of this sun. ¹²For you did it secretly, but I will do this thing before all Israel, before the sun.'"

¹³Then David said to Nathan, "I have sinned against the LORD."

And Nathan said to David, "The LORD has put away your sin; you shall not die. ¹⁴"However, because by this deed you have given great occasion to the enemies of the LORD to blaspheme, the child also who is born to you shall surely die." ¹⁵Then Nathan departed to his house. And the Lord struck the child that Uriah's wife bore to David, and it became very ill.

2 Samuel 12:1-15

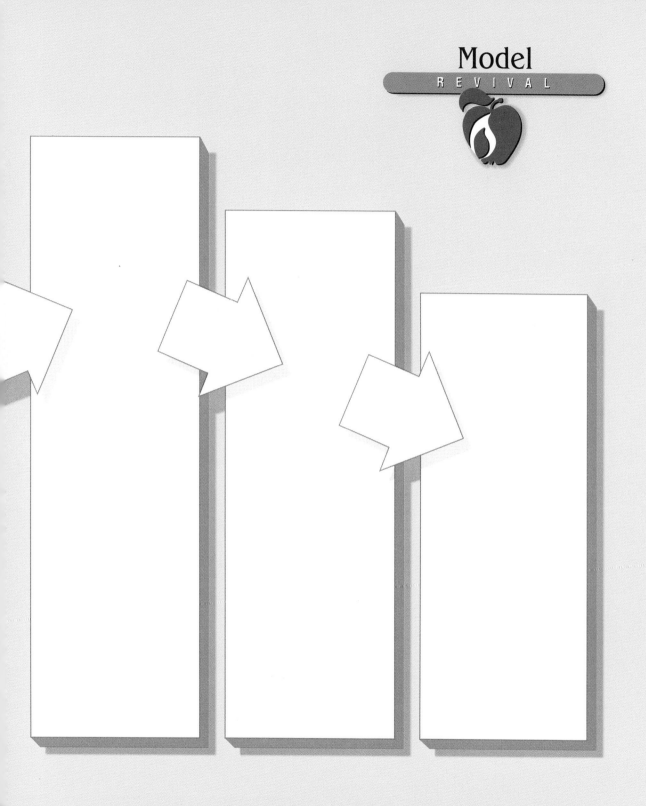

Model

R E V I V A L

Maxims

Revival Maxim 1:

Revival is spiritual restoration and is the spiritual teacher's _____

"A teacher affects eternity; he can never tell where his influence stops."
– Henry Brooks Adams

Revival Maxim 2:

Revival is only possible for those who have first experienced the second _____

Revival Maxim 3:

Revival is not a completed event but a continuing _____

"Revival consists of nothing less than a new beginning of obedience to God."
– Charles G. Finney

Revival Maxim 4:

Revival can occur in the life of an individual, group, or _____

Revival Maxim 5:

Revival always requires true repentance and the forsaking of known _____

Revival Maxim 6:

Revival always results in seeking and serving Christ with renewed _____

"If anything is true about the central theme of the Scriptures, it is that a loving God died to bring peace, holiness, and a personal relationship to His people. Our teaching, therefore, must call for the salvation of the lost, the holiness of the saved, and the personal walk with God for all who are called by His Name."
– Dr. Bruce Wilkinson

Revival Maxim 7:

Revival reestablishes life's central priority

_____

Revival Meaning

" _____ _____ _____ "

The teacher should encourage an ongoing personal revival in students' lives.

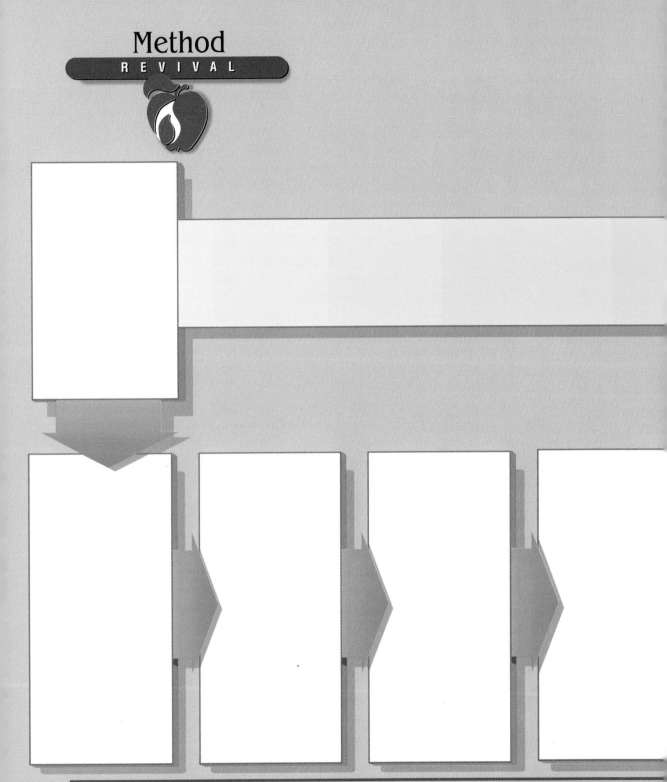

Method

REVIVAL

Maximizers

 R ealize that revival is needed by most Christians most of the _____

 E arnestly seek revival through intense and persistent private and public

_____

"Whatever applications we may make, whatever needs we may address, whatever content we may teach, the crown of it all is found when the heart reaches upward to God and God alone."
– Dr. Bruce Wilkinson

 V ary your delivery according to your students' spiritual _____

 I nstruct your students in the knowledge and practice of the spiritual

_____

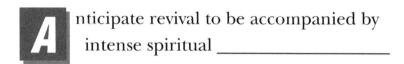

Verbalize the final call for commitment clearly and _____

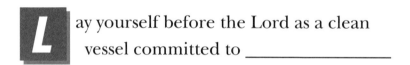

Anticipate revival to be accompanied by intense spiritual _____

Lay yourself before the Lord as a clean vessel committed to _____

Mastery

REVIVAL

MODEL:

1 Review the APL Revival Model and think again through the Biblical account of David and Nathan in 2 Samuel 12:1-15. Have you ever been confronted by another person in this way because of a sin in your life? Or have you confronted another person over his sin? If you can think of an incident like this, try to recall whether these five steps were followed. What was the result of the confrontation? Were any steps skipped? If so, how do you think that affected the outcome?

SPECIAL NOTE:

Each of these thought-provoking questions is related to one of the major segments of the Law of Revival. They are structured to help you internalize the true APL mindset.

MAXIMS:

2 Revival occurs in the life of the believer usually as a result of one of two things. The first is when the Christian becomes convicted of some known sin, confesses it to the Lord, and begins taking steps to restore godliness and holiness in his life. If that were to happen in your life this month, what sins would you begin dealing with first? In your class, what hindrances to godly living openly exist? What would have to take place for you and then your class to act on these issues?

3 The second thing that stimulates revival in addition to dealing with known sin is a renewed seeking after God. Even though Christians truly find the Lord when they are born again, they certainly have not "found" all of Him. But because this truth isn't widely understood, many Christians don't realize the need to continue seeking God. They stop rising early in order to seek Him through His Word and prayer. Remember, revival is relationship. So take some time to evaluate your present relationship with God, and the extent to which you are seeking Him. If deep down you want revival, then that relationship must be revitalized, either by taking away the negative (sin) or adding to the positive (fellowship with Him). Have you sought Him today? If you want help in your walk with God, contact Walk Thru the Bible Ministries (404-458-9300) and ask for a free copy of *The Daily Walk* and *Closer Walk* devotional guides. We made them for seekers.

METHOD:

4 As we saw in Step 1 of the APL Revival Method, the use of the Word of God is foundational to leading students to revival. In light of this, let's do some initial Biblical spadework to find out what God says about some particular sins your class may be dealing with. First, based on the needs of your students, list at least three of the sins you think are major problems in many of your students' lives. Then, using a concordance, Bible dictionary, or other tools, try to find at least two passages that relate to each sin. How could you help your students wrestle with those passages next time you teach?

5 Now take one of those sins you isolated in the question above and think through the next four steps of the APL Revival Method. Jot down some thoughts regarding how you would carry your students through each step in an effective, Biblical manner. Why not spend some time in prayer right now "preparing the ground" in your students' lives in this area?

MAXIMIZERS:

6 Consider your delivery when it comes to calling for commitment. Maximizer 3 encourages you to vary your delivery based on how your students are responding to your call. If they react in a strong, negative manner (indicated by their body language and verbal comments), you need to change your style; if they react tenderly and openly, you may need to become more tender yourself. Evaluate your own delivery in recent teaching situations. Have you used a suitable style to encourage them effectively? What will you do next time to (1) recognize their response better and (2) adjust your style appropriately?

7 The bottom line of this Law of Revival is that if you want to see your students in revival, then you must be in revival. Look again at the final Maximizer. Consider taking that crucial step this very moment. If you do, spend some time in prayer with the Father to talk it over with Him. Then sign your name in the margin and write the date. Prepare yourself for some exciting teaching opportunities in the days ahead!

To get the most out of these questions, take the time to think through them, then capture your thoughts in a journal or notebook. Or get together with several other people attending this APL course and discuss your answers.

Memory
R E V I V A L

The Law of Revival

" _____ _____ _____ "

Step 1: _____

Step 2: _____

Step 3: _____

Step 4: _____

Step 5: _____

I commit to _____

_____

_____

APL

APPENDICES

Introducing The 7 Laws of the Teacher™ Video Series with Dr. Howard G. Hendricks

One of America's foremost Christian educators shows you how to teach for lifechange!

Whether you are a pastor, Sunday school teacher, Bible study leader, school teacher, or parent, let Dr. Howard G. Hendricks—Christian educator, author, master communicator—show you how to teach with lifechanging impact. Discover The 7 Laws of the Teacher and unleash your effectiveness as a communicator of Biblical truth.

Presented by Walk Thru the Bible Ministries, this seven-part video series has been developed as a companion series to The 7 Laws of the Learner by Dr. Bruce Wilkinson. Together these seminars are designed to help anyone who teaches become more skillful with greater results.

The seven principles Dr. Hendricks explains in this innovative video series can revolutionize your communication skills:

- The Law of the Teacher
- The Law of Education
- The Law of Activity
- The Law of Communication
- The Law of the Heart
- The Law of Encouragement
- The Law of Readiness

It's the perfect follow-up series to The 7 Laws of the Learner, and it features Dr. Hendricks—a trailblazing Christian educator who practices what he preaches—on video. The series comes complete with a Leader's Guide for discussion and application, a Course Notebook to enable viewers to get the most out of the series, and a textbook by Dr. Hendricks.

For information on how you can benefit from this exciting video series, available now, contact **Walk Thru the Bible Ministries, P.O. Box 80587, Atlanta, Georgia 30366; telephone (404) 458-9300.**

Congratulations on taking this important step in your teaching career! By participating in this 7 Laws of the Learner Seminar, you have made a commitment to hone your teaching skills for a more effective, lifelong teaching ministry.

To recognize your commitment and achievement, Walk Thru the Bible Ministries has prepared a beautiful APL Certificate of Achievement, personalized and suitable for framing. And it's absolutely free! This certificate is printed in three colors on fine paper, and features a gold embossed seal. And your name will be specially imprinted on it!

Simply complete the form on the reverse side of this page and return it to your leader, or mail it to:

APL Certificate
Walk Thru the Bible Ministries
P.O. Box 80587
Atlanta, Georgia 30366

Your certificate will be sent by return mail. Please allow six to eight weeks for receipt.

NOTE: Be certain to print clearly. Write your name *exactly* as you want it to appear on the certificate.

Again, our congratulations for completing this exciting step of teacher training. Your adventure in teaching is just beginning!

APL Certificate of Achievement Order Form

FREE OFFER!
Please complete the form on the next page and return it to your group leader. You'll receive by mail a beautiful APL Certificate of Achievement for attending The 7 Laws of the Learner Seminar!

Certificate of Achievement Order Form

Please print your responses below and return this form to your teacher. We will send you an official Certificate of Achievement, suitable for framing, for completing The 7 Laws of the Learner course, part of the Applied Principles of Learning Curriculum.

CAREFULLY PRINT YOUR NAME EXACTLY AS YOU WANT IT TO APPEAR ON YOUR CERTIFICATE. BE SURE TO ANSWER ALL QUESTIONS .

Name ————————————————————————

Address ————————————————————————

City/State/Zip————————————————————

Phone: Home ( ) ———————— Office ( ) ————————

Occupation ———————— Name of Church ————————

Denomination ———————— Avg. # Sunday A.M. Attendance ————

Your Age:
☐ 18 or below
☐ 19-25
☐ 26-40
☐ 41-55
☐ 56 or above

1 What group(s) have you taught? (check all that apply)
☐ Sunday morning sermon ☐ Sunday evening sermon ☐ Wednesday evening service
☐ Sunday school class ☐ Church Bible study group ☐ Home Bible study group
☐ School classes ☐ College classes ☐ Graduate classes
☐ Family ☐ Other (please specify): ————————

2 What age group(s) are you currently teaching? (check all that apply)
☐ Preschool or Kindergarten ☐ Young Adult
☐ Grades 1-6 ☐ Middle Adult
☐ Grades 7-12 ☐ Senior Adult
☐ College ☐ Mixed Ages

3 How did you find out about The 7 Laws of the Learner Seminar?
☐ Received mailing at home ☐ Saw newspaper announcement
☐ Received brochure at church ☐ Saw brochure/poster at Christian bookstore
☐ Received brochure from a ministry ☐ Pastor/church leader invited me
   (e.g., Campus Crusade, Navigators) ☐ Other: ————————
☐ Heard radio announcement ————————

4 How would you rate The 7 Laws of the Learner on a scale of 1-10?
(Circle your response—10 = excellent rating, 1 = poor rating):
a. The Course Teacher (Name_____) 1 2 3 4 5 6 7 8 9 10
b. The Course Notebook 1 2 3 4 5 6 7 8 9 10
c. The Course Content 1 2 3 4 5 6 7 8 9 10

5 Please add your comments about "The 7 Laws of the Learner" Series (how you benefited from it, suggestions for improvement, why you did or did not enjoy it): ————————

————————————————————————

————————————————————————